BEAUTIFUL
BELLAS

Stacy McAnulty

ILLUSTRATED BY / ILUSTRADO POR
Joanne Lew-Vriethoff

SCHOLASTIC INC.

Originally published in English by Running Press Kids as *Beautiful*

Translated by Eida de la Vega

Text copyright © 2016 by Stacy McAnulty
Illustrations copyright © 2016 by Joanne Lew-Vriethoff
Translation copyright © 2017 by Scholastic Inc.

ISBN 978-1-338-19020-5

10 9 8 7 6   19 20 21

Printed in the U.S.A.   40
First Scholastic Bilingual printing 2017

For PAIGE and ELLERIE—AUNT STACY

For MAX WU YEN,
my baby girl, my inspiration—J.L.V.

A PAIGE y ELLERIE —TÍA STACY

A MAX WU YEN,
mi chiquitina, mi inspiración —J.L.V.

Beautiful girls . . .
Las chicas bellas...

... have the perfect look.
tienen un aspecto perfecto.

Beautiful girls
move gracefully.

Las chicas bellas
se mueven con gracia.

And light up every room.

E iluminan cualquier lugar.

Beautiful girls know all about makeup.
Las chicas bellas saben de maquillaje.

And have a smart style.

Y tienen un estilo inteligente.

Beautiful girls smile sweetly.

Las chicas bellas sonríen con dulzura.

And keep their hair properly in place.

Y mantienen el pelo donde debe estar.

Beautiful girls smell like flowers.
Las chicas bellas huelen a flores.

And sound like songbirds.

Y suenan como pájaros cantores.

Beautiful girls love to look in the mirror.

A las chicas bellas les encanta mirarse al espejo.

And to spend time with beautiful people.
Y estar en compañía de gente bella.

WOW!
¡BRAVO!

Beautiful girls deserve compliments.

Las chicas bellas merecen elogios.

STUNNING!
¡FABULOSO!

Because they make the world…

Porque hacen el mundo…

BEAUTIFUL BELLO